'Let's jump to it, Glen Club. If we win, it's the Kids' Grand Slam Cup to us,' Mr Strom said. The Glen Club kids put on the club's red strip.

1

Dan limps up. His leg is in a splint. He is fed up and in a strop. 'Mr. Strom, my leg is stiff and I can't run.'

'Hmmm,' said Mr Strom. 'Dan runs the best. If Dan
can't run, can we still win?'

'Brad, can you run well? Can you sprint?' Brad had just come to Glen Club.
'Yes, I can sprint a bit,' said Brad.

A bus pulls up. Ten Cliff Club kids strut off the bus
and on to the grass.
'Not too bad,' says Brad.

Off the bus clumps a big, big lad. Brad blinks. 'Is he a prop?'
Rob asks, 'Is he just ten? All the Glen Club kids are ten or less.'

The big lad grabs Rob's hand and grins. 'I'm Sprog. I'm a prop and I'm just ten.'

Cliff Club win the toss. A small tap and the ball is
up. ZIP! It's lost to Glen Club's Jaz. Next, it's a pass
to the stand-off, Tim. CLUMP! Sprog hits Tim.

A Cliff Club kid trips and drops the ball. Jaz grabs it and slips a pass to Rob. BUMP! Sprog rams into Rob. The ball spins off into the stands.

Cliff Club toss the ball in. Brad jumps up, grabs it
and sprints off. He is swift, but the ref stops him.
'The ball went to the left,' the ref says. 'It's a scrum.'

Sprog slumps in the scrum and it comes down.
'You can't pull down the scrum,' yells the ref, 'or I will send you off!'

Fran has the next ball and runs off. Sprog's hit lifts her up and dumps her on the grass.

As Fran gets up, Sprog stamps on her leg.
'You can't stamp on legs!' yells the ref. 'Go to the sin
bin!' Sprog sulks and slinks off.

Brad said, 'I've got a plan. We can still win. Let's split up.' Rob got the ball and ran up the left. Brad crept past all the Cliff Club kids.

Rob taps the ball up and sends it across to Brad. Brad clamps it in his hands. He sprints to the end and flops down on the ball. It's a win for Glen Club!

Fran straps up her leg. She limps up to Dan, winks and hands him the Kids' Grand Slam Cup.
Dan just grins.